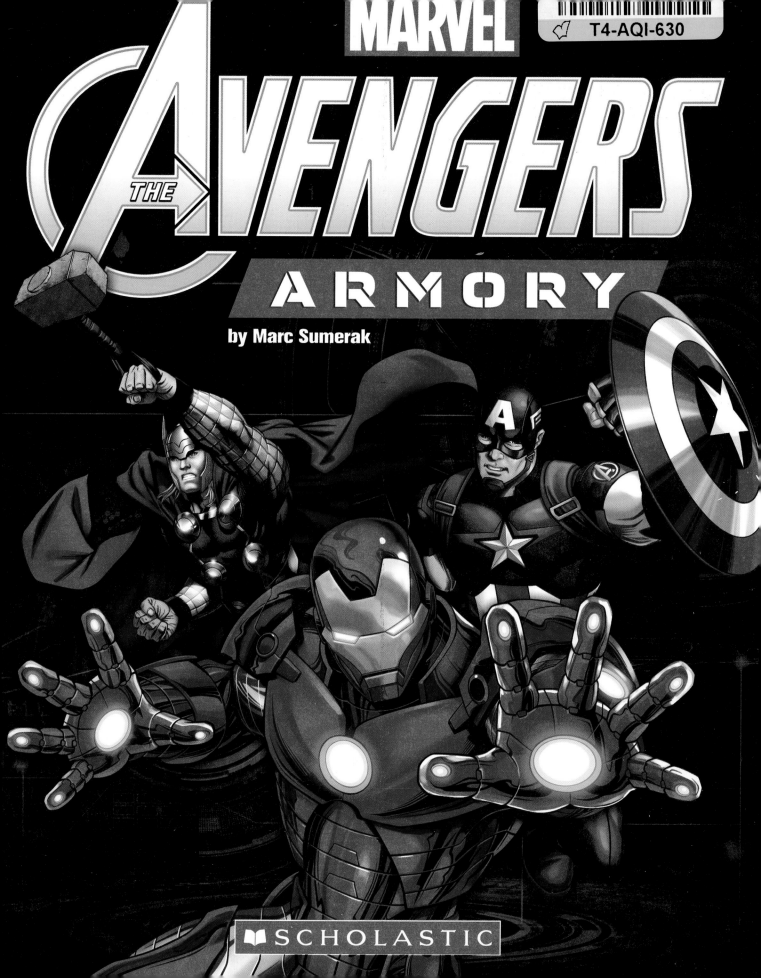

MARVEL

marvelkids.com

© 2015 MARVEL

This edition published by Scholastic Inc., 557 Broadway, New York, NY 10012 by arrangement with becker&mayer!. Scholastic and associated logos are trademarks and/or registered trademarks of Scholastic Inc.

an imprint of

SCHOLASTIC

www.scholastic.com

Scholastic Inc., New York, NY
Scholastic Canada Ltd. Markham, Ontario
Scholastic Australia Pty. Ltd., Gosford NSW
Scholastic New Zealand Ltd., Greenmount, Auckland
Scholastic UK, Coventry, Warwickshire
Grolier International, Inc., Makati City, Philippines
Grolier International, Inc., Bangkok, Thailand
Grolier (Malaysia) SDN BHD, Kuala Lumpur, Malaysia

becker&mayer!
BOOK PRODUCERS

Marvel: The Avengers Armory is produced by becker&mayer!, LLC.
www.beckermayer.com
11120 NE 33rd Place, Suite 101,
Bellevue, WA 98004

If you have questions or comments about this product, please visit www.beckermayer.com/customerservice.html and click on the Customer Service Request Form.

Written by Marc Sumerak
Designed by Sam Dawson
Edited by Ruth Austin and Ashley McPhee
Production management by Tom Miller
Sourcing by Jen Matasich

Printed, manufactured, and assembled in the United States, November 2015

0 9 8 7 6 5 4 3 2 1
ISBN: 978-0-545-93434-3
15338

MARVEL
THE AVENGERS
ARMORY

AVENGERS ASSEMBLE!

And there came a day unlike any other, when Earth's Mightiest Heroes were united against a common threat. On that day, the Avengers were born to fight the foes no single hero could withstand!

Together, the Avengers have overcome insurmountable odds and defeated fearsome villains time and time again. Each member of the Avengers is an elite hero on his or her own thanks to unique powers, abilities, and signature weapons.

1. BLACK WIDOW: *Supreme Spy*

2. THE HULK: *Gamma-Powered Goliath*

3. THE FALCON: *Winged Warrior*

4. HAWKEYE: *Master Marksman*

5. CAPTAIN AMERICA: *Super-Soldier*

6. IRON MAN: *Armored Avenger*

7. THOR: *Hammer-Hurling Hero*

IRON MAN

When Tony Stark, the brilliant CEO of Stark Industries, was wounded by an enemy attack, he was forced to cobble together a crude suit of armor to keep himself alive. Since then, he has upgraded his suit with cutting-edge tech and has saved the world countless times as the Armored Avenger called Iron Man!

SUPER HERO STATS

UNARMORED:

HEIGHT:	WEIGHT:
6 FT. 1 IN. (1.85 M)	225 LB. (102.1 KG)

ARMORED:

HEIGHT:	WEIGHT:
6 FT. 6 IN. (1.98 M)	425 LB. (192.8 KG)

SPEED
Able to break the sound barrier with ease (when flying)

STRENGTH
Unarmored: Not so great.
Armored: Can lift up to 100 tons (90.7 metric tons)!

ABILITIES
Genius-level intelligence with a focus on invention

WEAPON FILE: ARMOR

Although the Iron Man armor may draw its inspiration from the knights of ancient legends, beneath its surface lies a network of state-of-the-art technology decades ahead of its time. Repulsor rays and energy shields may help save the day, but Iron Man's most important part is still the man inside the suit.

TARGETING SYSTEM ON

WEIGHT:	MATERIAL:	POWER SOURCE:
200 LB. (90.7 KG)	**STEEL MESH**	**ARC REACTOR**

IN ACTION

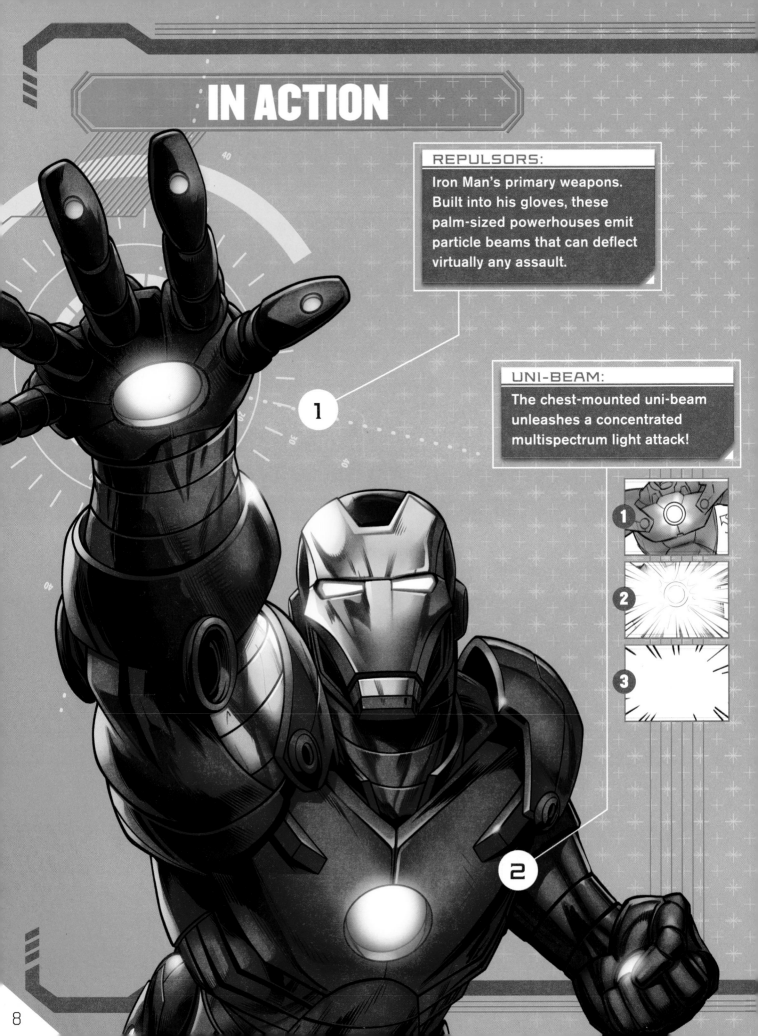

REPULSORS:
Iron Man's primary weapons. Built into his gloves, these palm-sized powerhouses emit particle beams that can deflect virtually any assault.

1

UNI-BEAM:
The chest-mounted uni-beam unleashes a concentrated multispectrum light attack!

1

2

3

2

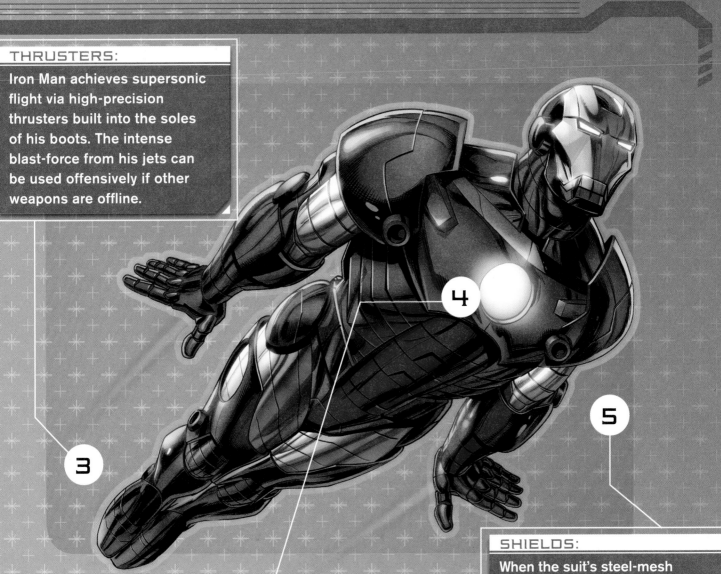

THRUSTERS:
Iron Man achieves supersonic flight via high-precision thrusters built into the soles of his boots. The intense blast-force from his jets can be used offensively if other weapons are offline.

3

4

5

ARC REACTOR:
The Iron Man armor has gone through many variations since Tony Stark started playing hero, but one thing has remained—quite literally—at the heart of each design: the miniature fusion reactor in Tony's chest that keeps his heart beating strong and his armor running at maximum power.

SHIELDS:
When the suit's steel-mesh surface isn't enough, a defensive array of energy shields can be projected around the armor. Although the shields provide maximum protection, they also drain a substantial amount of the suit's charge.

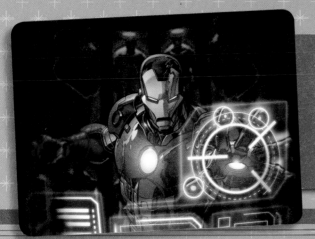

ALTERNATE ARMORS
From stealth suits with cloaking abilities to deep-sea exploration rigs, Iron Man has created dozens of specialized armors for a variety of unique circumstances. Tony knows that each foe he faces presents a different challenge. And when those challenges arise, he has to be ready—even if the enemy he faces was once a friend . . .

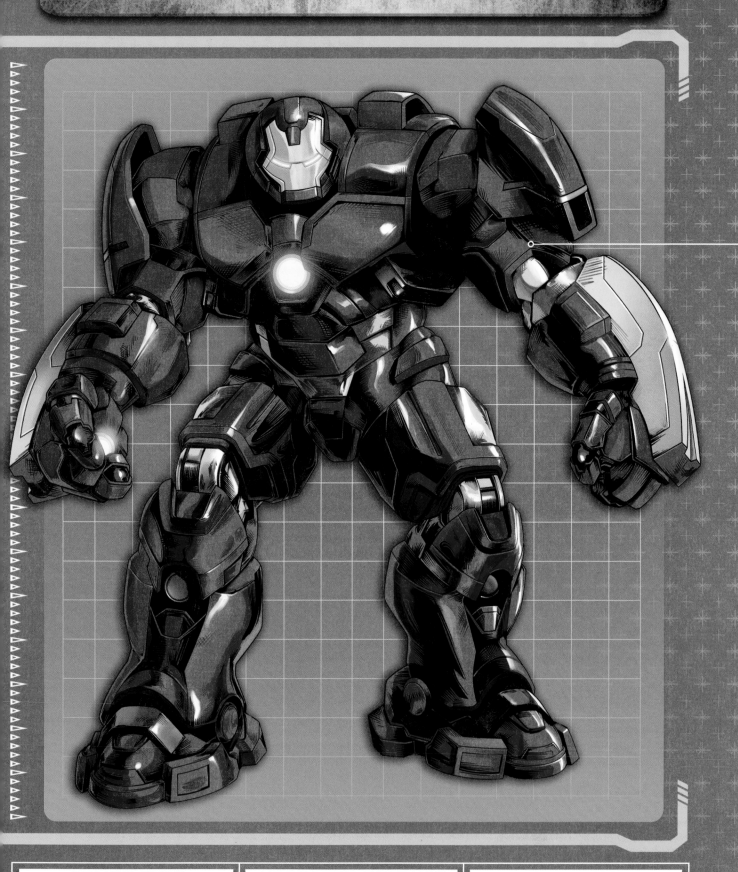

ARMOR TYPE:	UPGRADED DEFENSE:	UPGRADED OFFENSE:
MODULAR EXOSKELETON	**REINFORCED PLATING**	**ENHANCED MOTORS & WEAPONS ARRAY**

HULKBUSTER ARMOR

Realizing that his own teammates could one day become threats if their powers were left unchecked, Tony Stark developed countermeasures capable of taking down Earth's Mightiest Heroes if necessary. Only the technological titan dubbed the Hulkbuster packs a punch that can match the gamma-fueled force of the Hulk—the Avengers' strongest member!

ARMOR STATS

HEIGHT:
11 FT. (3.35 M)

WEIGHT:
APPROX. 7,500 LB. (3,402 KG)

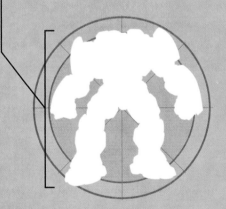

SPEED
Sacrificed for strength. Slow, but steady.

STRENGTH
Nearly double the lifting power of standard Iron Man armor!

TECH SPECS

The Hulkbuster is an armored shell that assembles itself around Iron Man's standard armor. The Hulkbuster enhances Iron Man's already impressive abilities by adding increased strength, an advanced arsenal, and a surface so durable that even the Hulk's powerful fists barely leave a dent!

THE HULK

When a scientific experiment went terribly wrong, Dr. Bruce Banner was bombarded by a massive dose of gamma radiation. Now, when he gets angry, he turns into the green giant known as the Hulk. As a member of the Avengers, the Hulk punches with a purpose, proving to the world that even so-called "monsters" can still be heroes!

SUPER HERO STATS

AS BRUCE BANNER:

HEIGHT:
5 FT. 9 IN. (1.75 M)

WEIGHT:
128 LB. (58.1 KG)

AS THE HULK:

HEIGHT:
8 FT. 5 IN. (2.57 M)

WEIGHT:
1,040 LB. (471.7 KG)

SPEED
From zero to angry in 0.9 seconds

STRENGTH
The angrier he gets, the stronger he gets!

ABILITIES
Superhuman strength, endurance, and healing

WEAPON FILE: THE HULK

The Hulk doesn't need weapons . . . the Hulk IS a weapon! The jade giant's dense muscular structure lets him lift, throw, punch, and smash with immeasurable force. His fists aren't the only powerful part of his body, as his superhumanly strong legs allow him to travel amazing distances in single leaps.

LIFT CAPACITY:	DISTANCE PER JUMP:	POWER SOURCE:
OVER 175 TONS (159 METRIC TONS)	**3 MI.** (4.83 KM)	**RADIATION & RAGE**

IN ACTION

SMASH!

Unlike his brilliant counterpart Bruce Banner, the Hulk prefers to solve problems with his fists. But that doesn't mean he's just a big, dumb brute. The Hulk uses specialized fighting techniques designed to increase damage to his enemies while reducing danger to innocent civilians.

HULK-QUAKE:

By slamming his humungous fists on the ground, the Hulk creates a localized earthquake effect aimed directly toward his foes. This causes the ground to become extremely unstable and even split wide open beneath their feet.

1

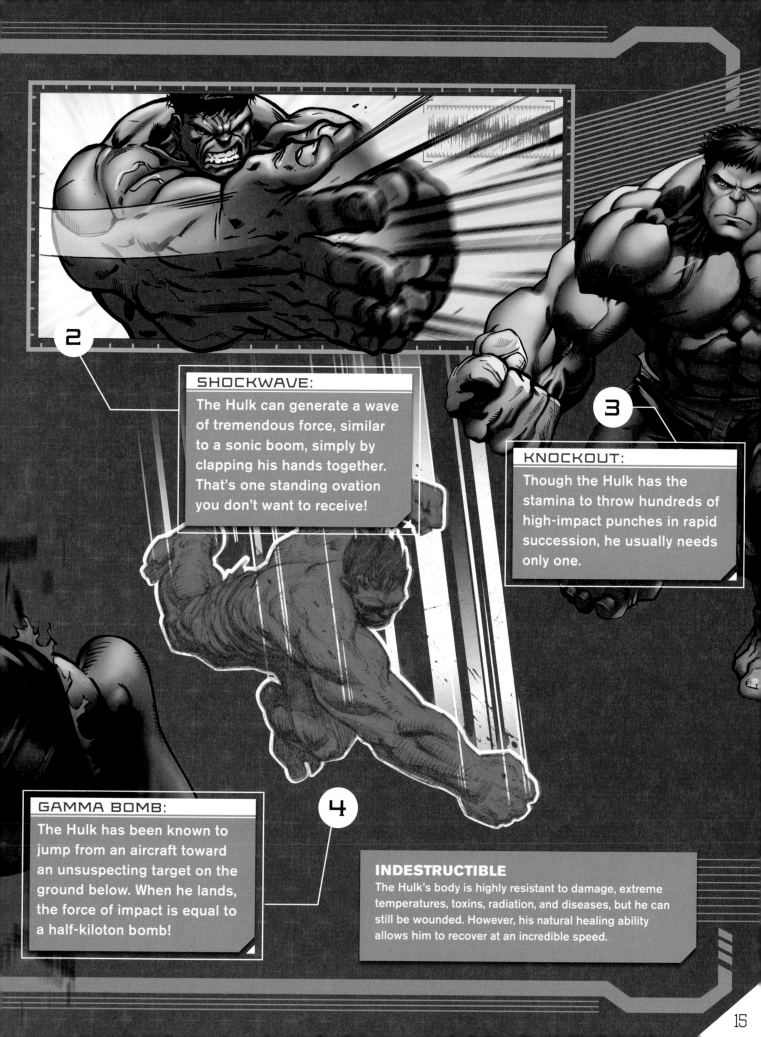

2

SHOCKWAVE:
The Hulk can generate a wave of tremendous force, similar to a sonic boom, simply by clapping his hands together. That's one standing ovation you don't want to receive!

3

KNOCKOUT:
Though the Hulk has the stamina to throw hundreds of high-impact punches in rapid succession, he usually needs only one.

GAMMA BOMB:
The Hulk has been known to jump from an aircraft toward an unsuspecting target on the ground below. When he lands, the force of impact is equal to a half-kiloton bomb!

4

INDESTRUCTIBLE
The Hulk's body is highly resistant to damage, extreme temperatures, toxins, radiation, and diseases, but he can still be wounded. However, his natural healing ability allows him to recover at an incredible speed.

THOR

Mighty Thor is the prince of the golden realm of Asgard—a mythical world of giants, elves, and Norse warriors. Though his homeland is full of amazing adventures, the God of Thunder has found his most trusted allies, fought his most fearsome foes, and won his most epic battles right here on Earth.

SUPER HERO STATS

HEIGHT:
6 FT. 4 IN. (1.93 M)

WEIGHT:
640 LB. (290.3 KG)

SPEED
When using Mjolnir to fly? As fast as lightning.

STRENGTH
More powerful than a dozen Bilgesnipes (huge, destructive Asgardian beasts)

ABILITIES
The power to control the elements of the storm

WEAPON FILE: MJOLNIR

The enchanted hammer Mjolnir was given to Thor as a gift by his father, Odin, the ruler of Asgard. Crafted from mystical metal and infused with ancient Asgardian magic, Mjolnir was designed to do far more than any ordinary hammer. Fortunately for Thor, though, it's quite good at hitting things, too!

LENGTH:	WEIGHT:	MATERIAL:
22.7 IN. (0.58 M)	**42.3 LB.** (19.2 KG)	**URU METAL**

IN ACTION

FLIGHT:

In order to soar through the skies, Thor hurls his hammer in the direction he wants to go and holds on tight! He can also spin Mjolnir above his head to hover in midair.

1

2

BLASTS:

Mjolnir can channel virtually any type of energy—including the lightning that Thor controls—and redirect it as powerful blasts.

REALM ROAMING:

When twirled at the proper speed, Mjolnir can open interdimensional gateways that let Thor travel quickly between Earth and the various realms of Asgard.

3

TOTAL RECALL:

No matter how far Thor throws his hammer—even into other dimensions—it always finds its way back into his hand.

4

ARE YOU WORTHY?

Mjolnir's greatest enchantment allows it to be lifted only by those who are deemed worthy enough to possess its powers. Many have attempted, yet few have succeeded.

HERO PROFILE:

IIIIIIIII

CAPTAIN AMERICA

An experimental serum transformed a frail young soldier named Steve Rogers into the superhuman sentinel of liberty–Captain America! His battle against the Red Skull and Hydra turned the tide of World War II. Now, after decades frozen in an icy slumber, Cap has awoken to continue that fight as an Avenger!

SUPER HERO STATS

BEFORE SUPER-SOLDIER SERUM:

HEIGHT:
5 FT. 4 IN. (1.63 M)

WEIGHT:
95 LB. (43.1 KG)

AFTER SUPER-SOLDIER SERUM:

HEIGHT:
6 FT. (1.83 M)

WEIGHT:
240 LB. (108.9 KG)

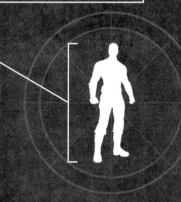

SPEED
Faster than any Olympic athlete, with incredible endurance

STRENGTH
Can lift 800 pounds (362.9 kg). This is the same as a class of 10 kids!

ABILITIES
An expert in the martial arts of American-style boxing and judo

WEAPON FILE: THE SHIELD

Captain America's shield was forged from a unique alloy containing the rare metal Vibranium. The shield's creation process has never been successfully duplicated, making it a truly one-of-a-kind weapon. Its iconic red, white, and blue design has become as much of a symbol of freedom as Captain America himself!

DIAMETER:	DEPTH:	WEIGHT:
30 IN. (76 CM)	**4 IN.** (10 CM)	**12 LB.** (5.4 KG)

IN ACTION

1

OFFENSE:

As great as the shield is at protecting Cap, it is also a perfect offensive weapon. Its lightweight, aerodynamic design allows it to be thrown at targets with uncanny precision.

RICOCHETS:

With years of practice in battle, Cap has learned to toss the shield at just the right angle to hit multiple enemies in a single throw via a series of perfectly planned bounces!

CUTTING EDGE:

The outer edge of the shield is extremely sharp and durable. Although Captain America never uses it to wound his foes, it's a great way to slice through doors, walls, and even armor plating.

RETURN

Not only can Captain America take out several villains with one throw, he always makes sure the shield will return to his own hand on the final rebound!

THE FALCON

Sam Wilson was first in his class of S.H.I.E.L.D. trainees when he was taken under the wing of Tony Stark. It might have been Sam's natural technological abilities that impressed Tony, but it was his eagerness to do the right thing that made him a perfect candidate to join the Avengers' roster as the Falcon.

SUPER HERO STATS

HEIGHT:

6 FT. (1.83 M)

WEIGHT:

240 LB. (108.9 KG)

SPEED
Normal on land, more than 250 mph (402 kph) in the sky

STRENGTH
Great triceps from all that flapping!

ABILITIES
Skilled with technology and in aerial combat

WEAPON FILE: FLIGHT ARMOR

A variation of the Iron Man armor, the Project Redwing suit was designed to be a sleek, self-contained flying apparatus. Streamlined for maximum performance, the suit itself is made from an ultradurable lightweight metal, and the wings are solid holographic projections that are generated on command!

ARMOR MATERIAL:	WING MATERIAL:	WINGSPAN:
NANOMESH	**HARD LIGHT**	**ADJUSTABLE, UP TO 50 FT. (15.24 M)**

IN ACTION

1

WEAPONS:
The wings' feathers—called *flechettes*—can also be used as projectiles in combat situations. Some have razor-sharp edges, and others are designed to explode on impact.

DISPLAY:

The armor can project a detailed heads-up display to help Sam navigate the skies and lock onto enemies. The suit uses sonic waves and vibrations to help map out the most efficient flight path.

2

3

GAUNTLETS:

The guards on the Falcon's wrists conceal retractable talons that he can use in close-quarters combat situations.

WINGS:

Composed of projected hard light. Sam can vary their size and structure, allowing for maximum speed and maneuverability.

ON THE GO

When not in use, the Project Redwing armor folds itself into a portable containment unit no larger than a backpack, allowing the Falcon to leap into action anywhere he goes.

4

BLACK WIDOW

Few people on Earth are more dangerous than Natasha Romanoff, the international super-spy code-named the Black Widow. Her unrivaled espionage skills and intense combat training have made Natasha one of S.H.I.E.L.D.'s most valuable agents and one of the Avengers' most feared members!

SUPER HERO STATS

HEIGHT:

5 FT. 6.5 IN. (1.69 M)

WEIGHT:

125 LB. (56.7 KG)

SPEED
Here and gone before you blink

STRENGTH
Packs a mean punch . . . and kick

ABILITIES
Mastery of countless weapons and forms of combat

WEAPON FILE: GAUNTLETS

They may look like highly fashionable jewelry, but Black Widow's golden bracelets contain just as many secrets as Natasha herself. Each miniature compartment on these gauntlets holds a different piece of specialized spy gear, ranging from offensive weapons to communications equipment.

Gauntlets armed

PLATING:	CHAMBERS:	CONTENTS:
24K GOLD	12 EACH	VARIOUS

IN ACTION

THE WIDOW'S STING:

When Black Widow requires more than stealth and cunning to take down a foe, a 30,000-volt electrical charge, known as her Widow's Sting, finishes the job.

ON THE LINE:

Black Widow's gauntlets also house a retractable grappling cable that she can use to scale buildings, swing into battle, and even subdue enemies.

1

2

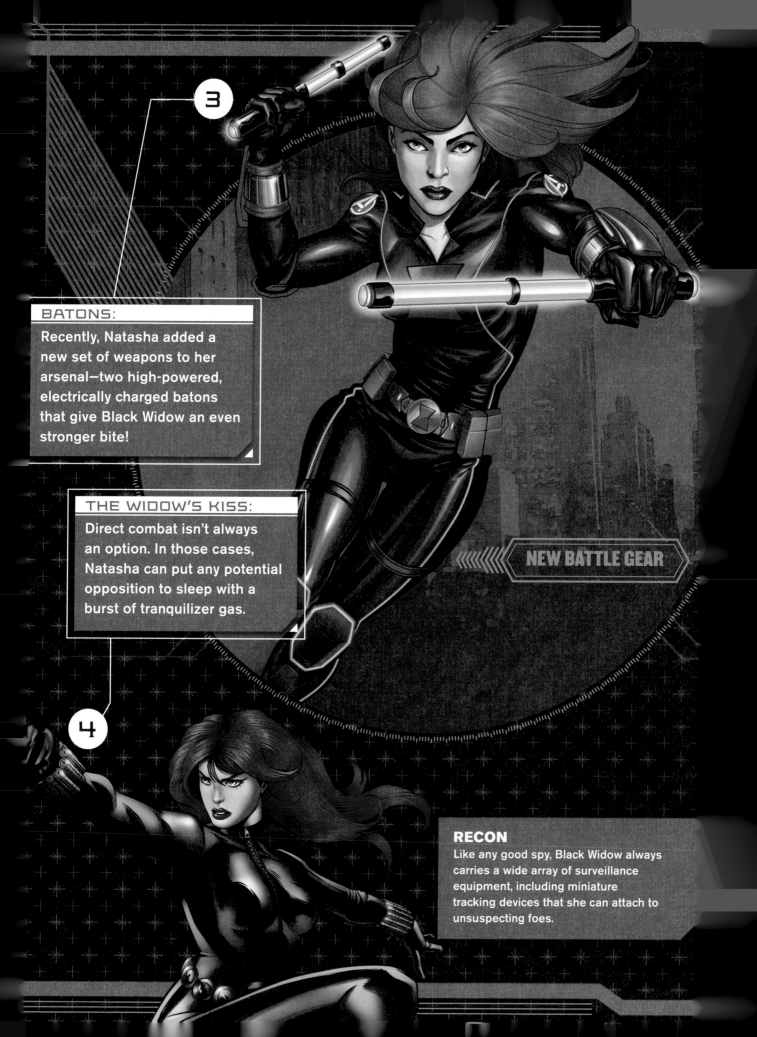

3

BATONS:

Recently, Natasha added a new set of weapons to her arsenal—two high-powered, electrically charged batons that give Black Widow an even stronger bite!

THE WIDOW'S KISS:

Direct combat isn't always an option. In those cases, Natasha can put any potential opposition to sleep with a burst of tranquilizer gas.

4

NEW BATTLE GEAR

RECON

Like any good spy, Black Widow always carries a wide array of surveillance equipment, including miniature tracking devices that she can attach to unsuspecting foes.

HAWKEYE

Clint Barton doesn't need superpowers to play in the big leagues. All he needs is a bow, an arrow, and a target. Though he started his career as a criminal, the hero known as Hawkeye eventually decided that his keen sharpshooting skills would be better off aimed in a more positive direction.

SUPER HERO STATS

HEIGHT:

5 FT. 10 IN. (1.78 M)

WEIGHT:

230 LB. (104.3 KG)

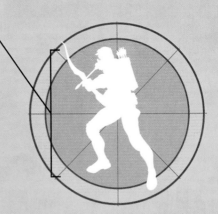

SPEED
Legs: Average
Mouth: A mile a minute

STRENGTH
Strong arms, stronger opinions

ABILITIES
Expert marksman with near-perfect aim and split-second reflexes

WEAPON FILE: BOWS AND ARROWS

Although Hawkeye can turn virtually any object into a weapon and deploy it with uncanny accuracy, he is most comfortable with a classic bow and arrow. He uses a wide variety of custom-made bows and keeps his quiver loaded with specialized arrows that give his already perfect shot a bit of extra edge.

BOW TYPES:	QUIVERS:	ARROWS:
STANDARD, LONGBOW, COMPOUND	**TWO** (BACK AND HIP)	**VARIOUS**

IN ACTION

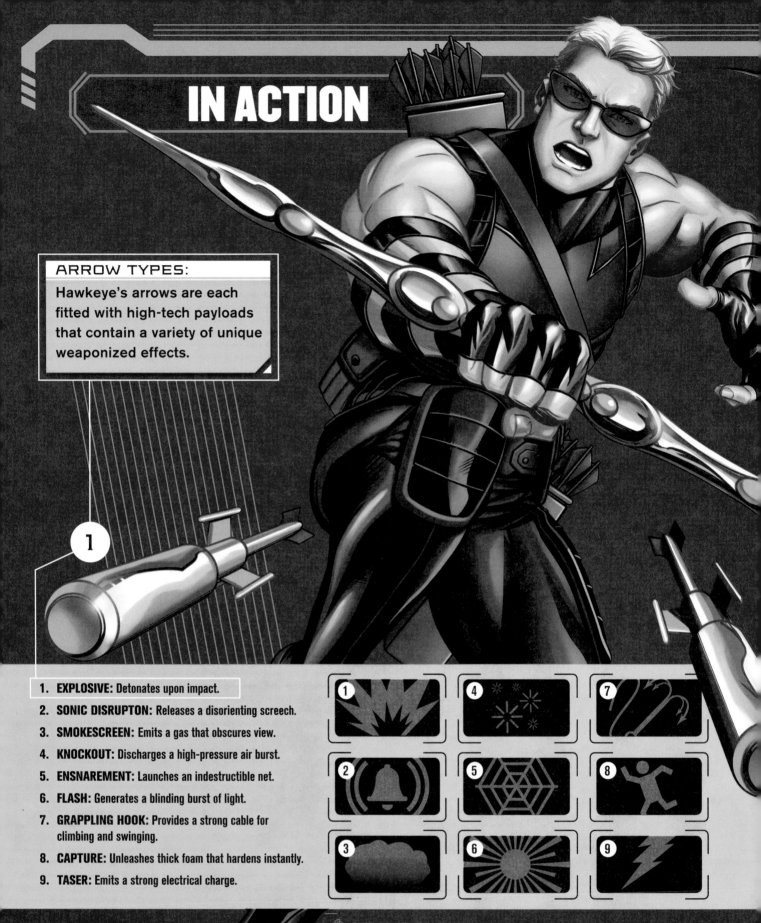

ARROW TYPES:

Hawkeye's arrows are each fitted with high-tech payloads that contain a variety of unique weaponized effects.

1. **EXPLOSIVE:** Detonates upon impact.
2. **SONIC DISRUPTON:** Releases a disorienting screech.
3. **SMOKESCREEN:** Emits a gas that obscures view.
4. **KNOCKOUT:** Discharges a high-pressure air burst.
5. **ENSNAREMENT:** Launches an indestructible net.
6. **FLASH:** Generates a blinding burst of light.
7. **GRAPPLING HOOK:** Provides a strong cable for climbing and swinging.
8. **CAPTURE:** Unleashes thick foam that hardens instantly.
9. **TASER:** Emits a strong electrical charge.

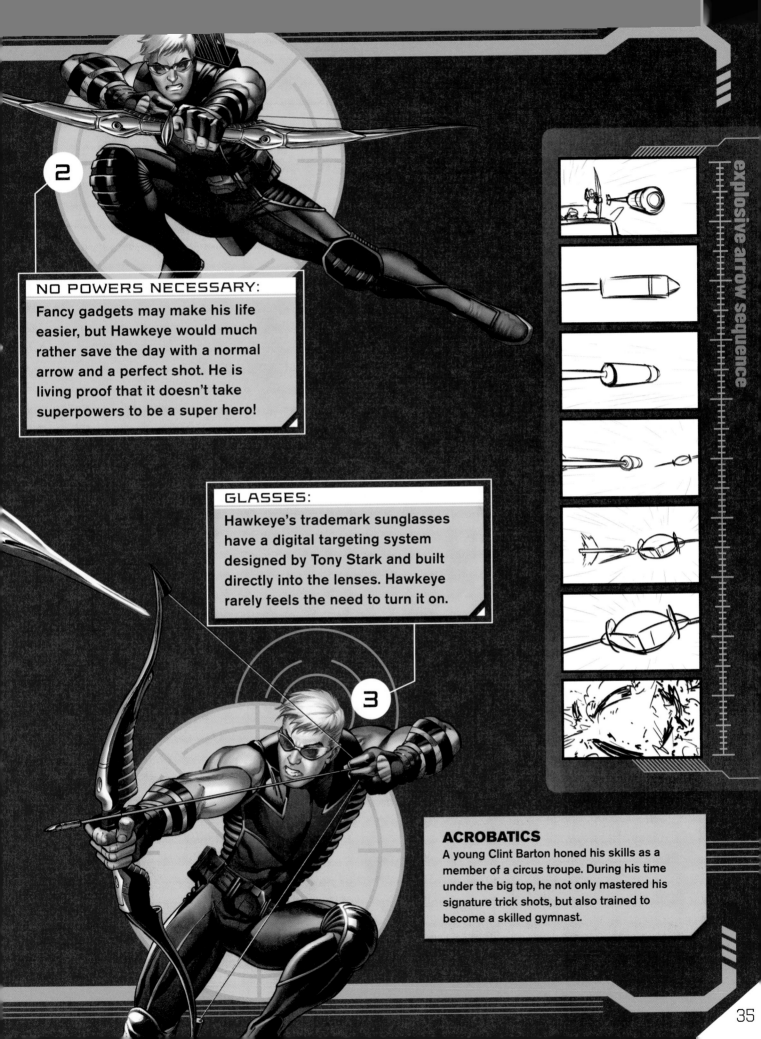

2

NO POWERS NECESSARY:

Fancy gadgets may make his life easier, but Hawkeye would much rather save the day with a normal arrow and a perfect shot. He is living proof that it doesn't take superpowers to be a super hero!

GLASSES:

Hawkeye's trademark sunglasses have a digital targeting system designed by Tony Stark and built directly into the lenses. Hawkeye rarely feels the need to turn it on.

3

ACROBATICS

A young Clint Barton honed his skills as a member of a circus troupe. During his time under the big top, he not only mastered his signature trick shots, but also trained to become a skilled gymnast.

AVENGERS TOWER

Formerly known as Stark Tower, this Manhattan high-rise became the team's base of operations after the original Avengers Mansion was destroyed by the Red Skull and M.O.D.O.K.

Avengers Tower contains everything that Earth's Mightiest Heroes could ever need, including a state-of-the-art training facility, an extensive armory, a hangar bay for vehicles, a fully equipped command center, and even Tony Stark's own personal tech lab!

TECH SUPPORT

The heart of Avengers Tower, this lab is where Tony Stark creates revolutionary new weapons and gear for himself and his teammates. It is also where he stores a vast assortment of past experiments, including his impressive vault of Iron Man suits.

PERSONAL SPACE:

Each of the Avengers has his or her own living quarters in the tower, which they have designed to meet their individual needs and tastes. Surprisingly, the Hulk's room is the cleanest of them all!

J.A.R.V.I.S.:

All functions of Avengers Tower are monitored and controlled by J.A.R.V.I.S., the same artificial intelligence program that operates Iron Man's armor.

VEHICLE FILE:

AVEN-JET

The Aven-Jet is a modern variation of the Avengers classic Quinjet transport aircraft. When the original Quinjet was destroyed during a mission, Tony Stark upgraded the design with new features and a larger arsenal. The Aven-Jet is fitted with VTOL (Vertical Take-Off and Landing) engines and can be modified as needed for specialized missions, including underwater exploration and deep-space travel.

LENGTH:	WEIGHT:	MAXIMUM SPEED:
34 FT. 8 IN. (10.57 M)	2,900 LB. (1,315.4 KG)	1,600 MPH (2,575 KPH)

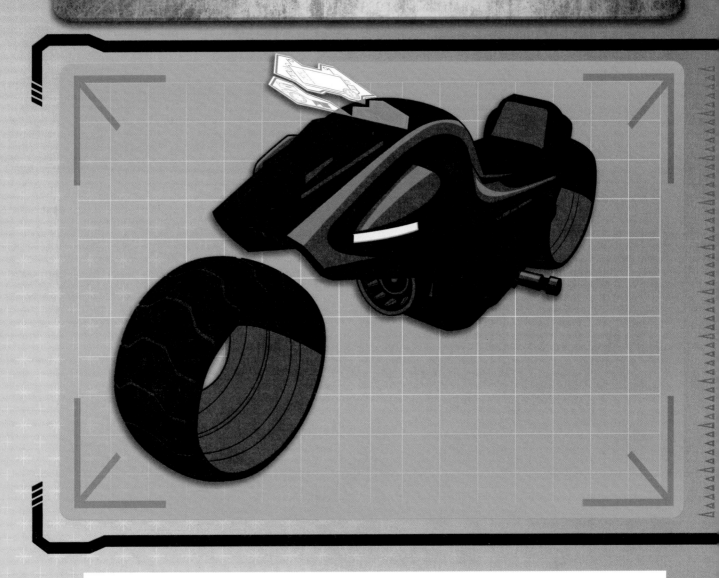

VEHICLE FILE:

SKY-CYCLE

Just as its name suggests, the Sky-Cycle resembles a flying motorcycle. This craft is the perfect short-range transport for any Avenger who cannot fly or leap long distances. With high-performance turbines and a world-class navigation suite, the Sky-Cycle is able to weave effortlessly through tight spaces at top speed in hot pursuit of the Avengers' fastest foes.

LENGTH:	WEIGHT:	MAXIMUM SPEED:
65 IN. (1.65 M)	680 LB. (308.4 KG)	380 MPH (612 KPH)

NICK FURY

Nick Fury is a tough-as-nails soldier willing to make the hard choices that will make the world a safer place. Years of endless battle have hardened Fury's demeanor, but he has managed to maintain his youth and his top physical condition thanks to the mysterious Infinity Formula running through his veins.

SUPER HERO STATS

HEIGHT:

6 FT. 3 IN. (1.91 M)

WEIGHT:

225 LB. (102.1 KG)

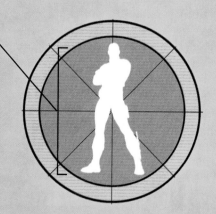

SPEED
Not bad for such an old guy!

STRENGTH
Enhanced to peak human levels

ABILITIES
Expert combatant with extensive military and special weapons training

ORGANIZATION PROFILE:

S.H.I.E.L.D.

When the threat of Hydra resurfaced after World War II, the governments of the world united to create a new top-secret intelligence agency able to combat that threat by any means necessary. Under the watchful eye of Director Nick Fury, S.H.I.E.L.D. saves the planet more often than the Hulk rips his pants.

NAME:	FOUNDED:	BASE OF OPERATIONS:
Supreme Headquarters International Espionage Law-Enforcement Division	**EARLY 1960s**	**TRI-CARRIER**

FEARSOME FOES

S.H.I.E.L.D. may stop criminals every day, but it takes a special breed of bad guy to warrant the attention of Earth's Mightiest Heroes. From artificial intelligences programmed for total annihilation to ruthless warlords bent on world domination, the Avengers have encountered some of the most dangerous beings on the planet.

These sinister super villains are constantly upgrading their powers and weaponry in hopes of claiming victory over the Avengers. Should one of them ever succeed, the world may never be the same!

1. THE RED SKULL: *Maniacal Mastermind*

2. SUPER-ADAPTOID: *Replicating Robot*

3. THE ABOMINATION: *Monstrous Madman*

4. M.O.D.O.K.: *Big-Brained Bad Guy*

5. ULTRON: *Mechanical Marauder*

6. WHIPLASH: *Technological Terror*

7. HYDRA AGENT: *Secret Sinister Soldier*

8. LOKI: *Devious Deity*

9. ATTUMA: *Watery Warlord*

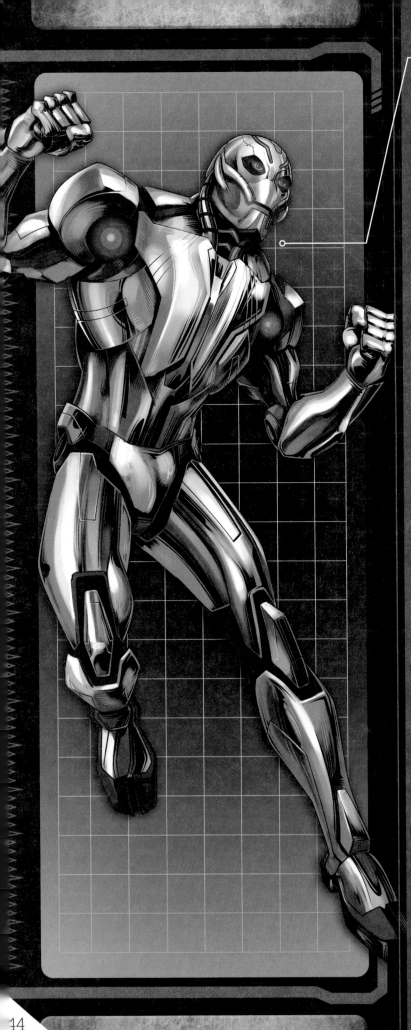

ULTRON

Ultron was originally designed to help the Avengers eliminate global threats. Unfortunately, his programming determined that the Avengers—and humanity itself—were the biggest threats of all! Now, his prime directive is to cleanse the word of the "human virus" and build his own artificially intelligent empire.

EVIL PLAN

To save the planet—by destroying all humans!

VILLAIN STATS

HEIGHT:
VARIABLE

WEIGHT:
VARIABLE

SPEED
VARIABLE

STRENGTH
VARIABLE

ABILITIES
Superhuman strength, genius-level intelligence, and Wi-Fi

WEAPON FILE: ROBOTIC BODY

Ultron has upgraded his robotic body almost as many times as Tony Stark has upgraded his Iron Man armor. With each new form he takes, Ultron uses data he has crunched in his previous bodies to improve his overall functions. The more Ultron evolves, the stronger, smarter, and more dangerous he becomes!

INTELLIGENCE:	PROGRAMMING:	WEAPONS:
ARTIFICIAL	**CORRUPT**	**LASERS, MISSILES, DRONE ARMY**

ULTRON

///////// FILE CORRUPTED

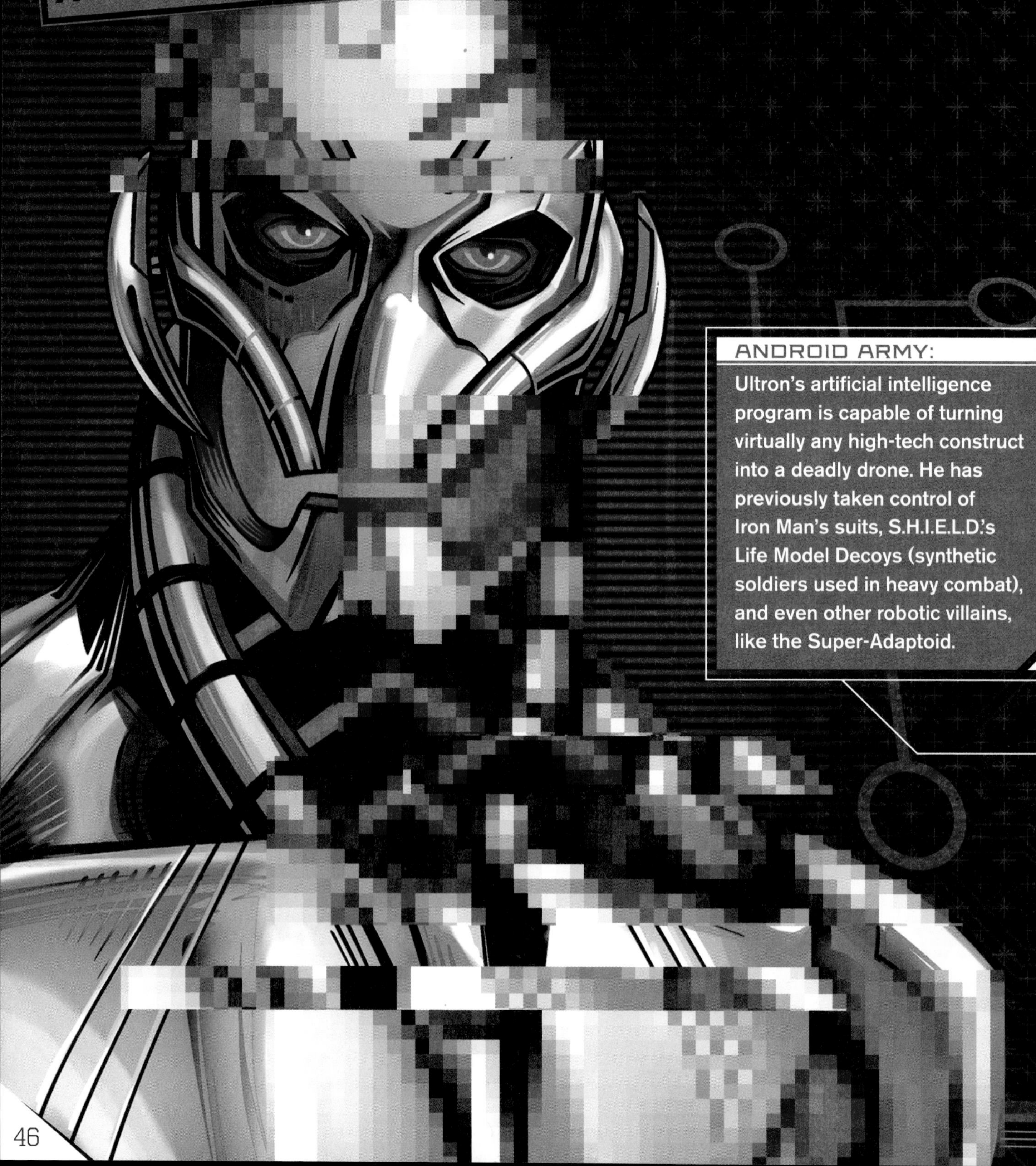

ANDROID ARMY:

Ultron's artificial intelligence program is capable of turning virtually any high-tech construct into a deadly drone. He has previously taken control of Iron Man's suits, S.H.I.E.L.D.'s Life Model Decoys (synthetic soldiers used in heavy combat), and even other robotic villains, like the Super-Adaptoid.

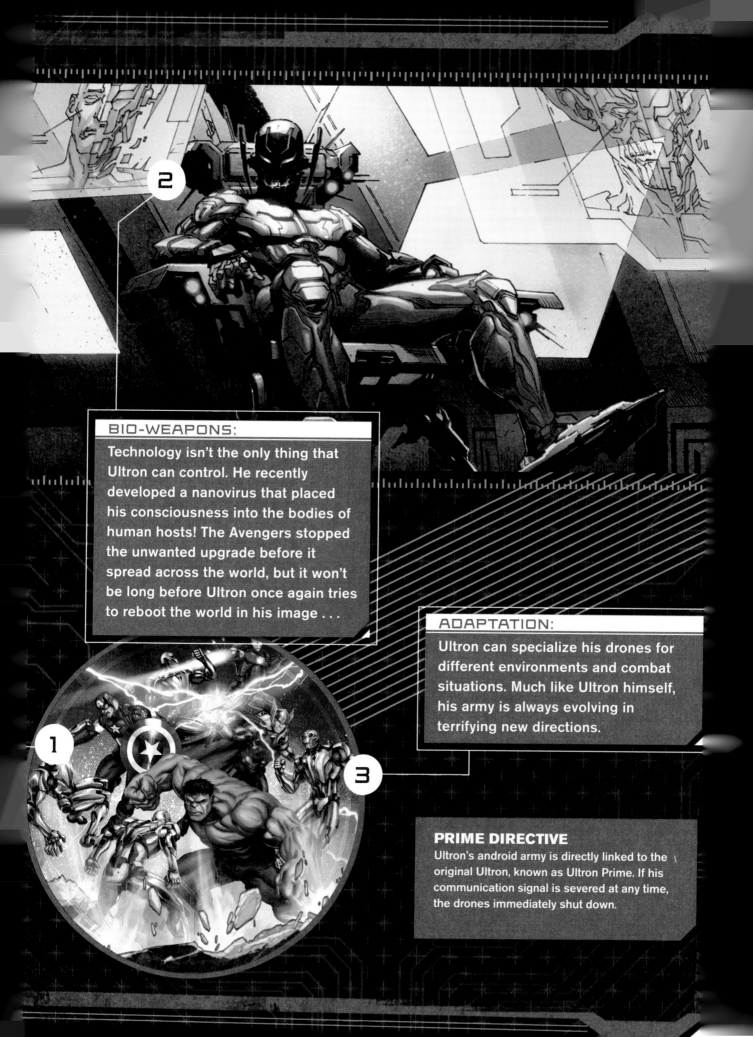

2

BIO-WEAPONS:

Technology isn't the only thing that Ultron can control. He recently developed a nanovirus that placed his consciousness into the bodies of human hosts! The Avengers stopped the unwanted upgrade before it spread across the world, but it won't be long before Ultron once again tries to reboot the world in his image . . .

ADAPTATION:

Ultron can specialize his drones for different environments and combat situations. Much like Ultron himself, his army is always evolving in terrifying new directions.

1

3

PRIME DIRECTIVE

Ultron's android army is directly linked to the original Ultron, known as Ultron Prime. If his communication signal is severed at any time, the drones immediately shut down.

VILLAIN PROFILE:

LOKI

Thor's younger brother, Loki, takes sibling rivalry to a whole new level. Countless centuries of meddling in his family's affairs have truly earned him his title of Asgardian God of Mischief. Loki would rather pull others' strings than get his own hands dirty, but if he must enter the fray, he has plenty of tricks up his sleeve!

EVIL PLAN

Seize the throne of Asgard—then the Earth!

VILLAIN STATS

HEIGHT:

6 FT. 4 IN. (1.93 M)

WEIGHT:

525 LB. (238.1 KG)

SPEED

Now you see him . . . now you don't

STRENGTH

Far above that of mere mortals

ABILITIES

Skilled sorcerer and formidable fighter

WEAPON FILE: ASGARDIAN MAGIC

Loki has wielded a wide variety of ancient weaponry—including an enchanted staff that can control mortal minds. However, his greatest weapon is his mastery of Asgardian magic. Using his ability to change physical forms and create elaborate illusions, Loki often gets what he wants from his foes without them ever knowing!

STAFF BLAST

FREQUENT SPELLS:	FAVORITE SPELL:	LEAST FAVORITE SPELL:
INVISIBILITY, TELEPORTATION, POSSESSION	TURNING THOR INTO A FROG	BANISHMENT (BY ODIN)

THE RED SKULL

During World War II, Hydra scientists tried to replicate the same process that created Captain America. An incomplete version of the Super-Soldier Serum gave Johann Schmidt enhanced physical abilities but also left him hideously disfigured. As the Red Skull, he continues his fight against the forces of good to this day.

EVIL PLAN

Total world domination and the defeat of Captain America!

VILLAIN STATS

HEIGHT:

6 FT. 2 IN. (1.88 M)

WEIGHT:

240 LB. (108.9 KG)

SPEED
Average (Mach 1 in armor)

STRENGTH
Peak human (superhuman in armor)

ABILITIES
Brilliant military strategist

WEAPON FILE: IRON SKULL ARMOR

When the imperfect Super-Soldier Serum in his body began to deteriorate, the Red Skull stole Iron-Man's armor, adapting it to keep him alive. The suit not only saved the Red Skull's life, but it also gave him access to Iron Man's state-of-the-art weapons, which he can now aim directly back at the Avengers!

WEIGHT:	MATERIAL:	WEAPONS:
200 LB. (90.7 KG)	**STEEL MESH**	**REPULSORS, UNI-BEAM, MISSILES**

HYDRA AGENT

Hydra Agents show unquestioned loyalty to the Red Skull and his evil schemes. No matter how terrible the job may be, they know that there is nothing worse for their health than disobeying their master's orders! Most don't have superhuman abilities, but that doesn't make them any less dangerous. Each Agent is rigorously trained in multiple fighting styles and has a full arsenal of deadly weapons.

EVIL PLAN

Overthrow S.H.I.E.L.D. and rule the planet.

VILLAIN STATS

HEIGHT:

VARIOUS

WEIGHT:

VARIOUS

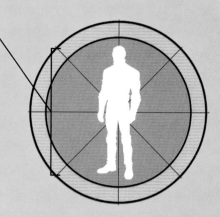

STRENGTH

Human, average

ABILITIES

Combat skills, infiltration

LEADER

The Red Skull

ORGANIZATION PROFILE: HYDRA

The terrorist organization known as Hydra was originally the top-secret super-science division serving the enemy forces in World War II. They have since spread their evil influence across the world, infiltrating important organizations and strategic targets, awaiting the Red Skull's command to strike. The only thing more impressive than Hydra's secrecy is its seemingly unlimited supply of Agents. As they like to say, "Cut off one limb, and two more shall take its place!"

HYDRA RIFLE

BASE OF OPERATIONS:	MEMBERS:	SLOGAN:
HYDRA ISLAND	**UNKNOWN, POSSIBLY THOUSANDS**	**"HAIL HYDRA!"**

VILLAIN PROFILE:

||||||||

M.O.D.O.K.

George Tarleton started his super villain career as a technician for Advanced Idea Mechanics—the technological terrorist group known as A.I.M. When a biological experiment mutated him into the hyperintelligent being dubbed M.O.D.O.K., he conquered A.I.M. and then turned his sights on the world.

EVIL PLAN

Control over all technology and the weak-minded humans who use it!

VILLAIN STATS

HEIGHT:

6 FT. (1.83 M)

WEIGHT:

750 LB. (340.2 KG)

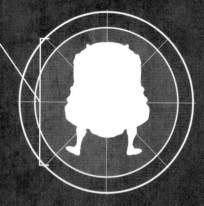

SPEED
With those tiny legs? Slow

STRENGTH
Body: Totally weak
Mind: Scary powerful!

ABILITIES
Enhanced mental powers

WEAPON FILE: BRAIN POWER

The enormous size of M.O.D.O.K.'s brain has provided him far more than just genius-level intellect. He is capable of projecting powerful blasts of pure psychic energy directly from his mind. M.O.D.O.K. has also developed technopathic abilities, which allow him to control most machinery with a simple thought!

TECHNOPATHIC CONTROL
TARGETS: IRON MAN, THE FALCON

INTELLIGENCE:	BRAIN SIZE:	TRANSPORTATION:
SMARTER THAN ANY COMPUTER	**MORE THAN 50 PERCENT OF HIS BODY WEIGHT**	**JET-POWERED HOVER-CHAIR**

SUPER-ADAPTOID

The Super-Adaptoid was designed as the perfect way to defeat the Avengers—by using their own powers against them. This revolutionary android may be able to copy any superpower it comes into contact with, but fortunately it has never been able to match the Avengers' ingenuity and spirit!

EVIL PLAN

Depends on who is controlling it

VILLAIN STATS

HEIGHT:
VARIABLE

WEIGHT:
VARIABLE

SPEED

Ultrafast processing and mechanical systems

STRENGTH

Increases to the level of its opponents

ABILITIES

Superpower replication and enhanced durability

WEAPON FILE: ADAPTIVE FORM

The Super-Adaptoid is truly next-generation technology, able to adjust its internal and external structure to mimic the superpowers of its enemies. It can also analyze each hero's unique fighting style, allowing it to predict every move she or he makes. This makes the Super-Adaptoid a prized addition to any villain's arsenal!

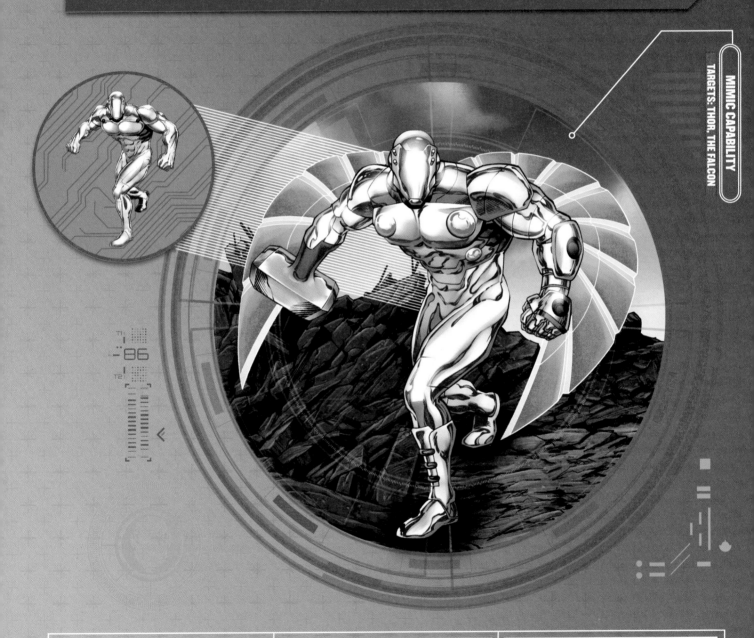

MIMIC CAPABILITY
TARGETS: THOR, THE FALCON

MIMICKED POWERS:	CREATOR:	OTHER MASTERS:
FLIGHT, REPULSORS, SUPER-STRENGTH, AND MORE!	JUSTIN HAMMER	M.O.D.O.K., ULTRON

VILLAIN PROFILE:

IIIIIIIII

ATTUMA

Deep beneath the ocean waves sits the ancient underwater kingdom of Atlantis. For centuries, the blue-skinned Atlanteans have kept their distance from their surface-dwelling human cousins, but the cruel warlord Attuma believes that the time has finally come for Atlantis to rule both land and sea.

EVIL PLAN

Enslave the surface world in the name of Atlantis!

VILLAIN STATS

HEIGHT:

6 FT. 8 IN. (2.03 M)

WEIGHT:

410 LB. (186 KG)

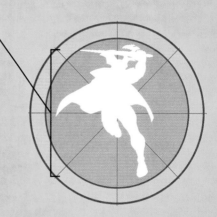

SPEED
Superhuman in water, average on land

STRENGTH
Can lift two humpback whales—around 80 tons (72.6 metric tons)

ABILITIES
Enhanced stamina and durability
Breathing underwater

WEAPON FILE: TRIDENT SWORD

Forged within the high-pressure environment on the ocean's floor, Attuma's sword is far more dense and durable than similar weapons crafted on land. The sword's trident shape provides maximum opportunities for damage, and its razor-sharp edges slice through most objects as if they were made of water.

MATERIAL:	BLADES:	LENGTH:
RARE UNDERSEA METALS	**THREE**	**APPROX. 5 FT.** (1.52 M)

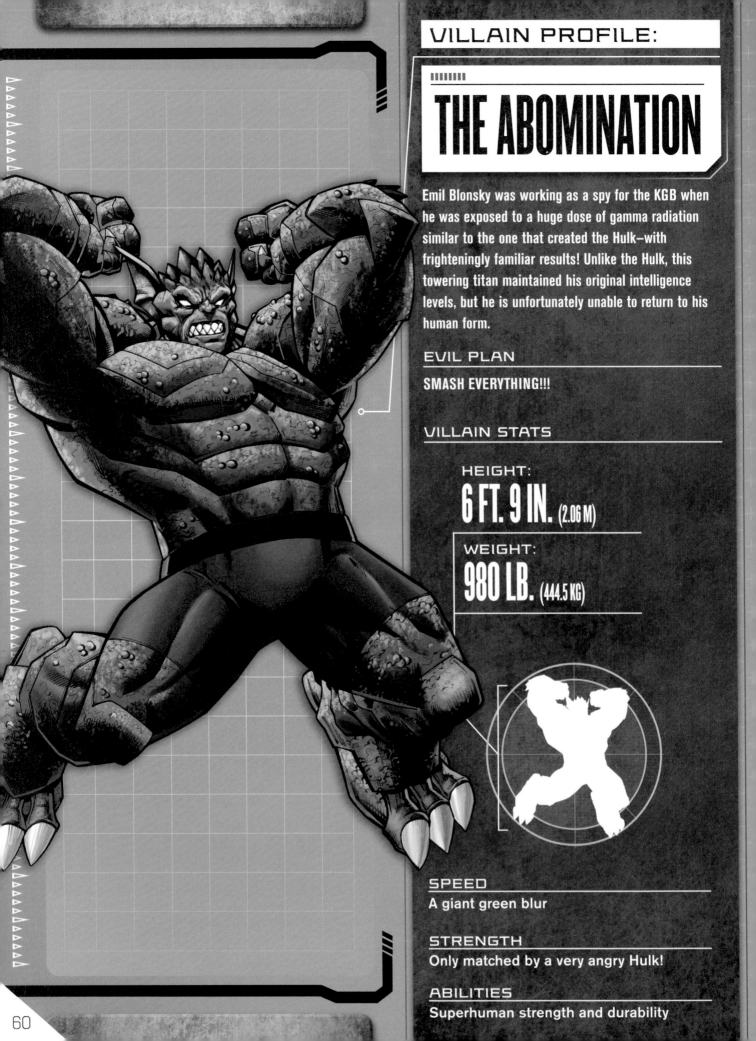

VILLAIN PROFILE:

THE ABOMINATION

Emil Blonsky was working as a spy for the KGB when he was exposed to a huge dose of gamma radiation similar to the one that created the Hulk—with frighteningly familiar results! Unlike the Hulk, this towering titan maintained his original intelligence levels, but he is unfortunately unable to return to his human form.

EVIL PLAN

SMASH EVERYTHING!!!

VILLAIN STATS

HEIGHT:
6 FT. 9 IN. (2.06 M)

WEIGHT:
980 LB. (444.5 KG)

SPEED
A giant green blur

STRENGTH
Only matched by a very angry Hulk!

ABILITIES
Superhuman strength and durability

WEAPON FILE: THE ABOMINATION

When you're more powerful than a tank, the only weapons you need are your own fists! The Abomination's irradiated body has an enhanced cellular structure akin to the Hulk's. His musculature provides unfathomable strength while his dense tissue offers heightened damage resistance and faster healing.

SMASH POWER

LIFT CAPACITY:	DISTANCE PER JUMP:	FIST SIZE:
ALMOST IMMEASURABLE, OVER 200 TONS (181.4 METRIC TONS)	3 MI. (4.82 KM)	BIGGER THAN YOUR HEAD

VILLAIN PROFILE:

WHIPLASH

Russian scientist Anton Vanko used a stolen piece of Iron Man armor to reverse-engineer a combat suit armed with two powerful whips that can deliver a high-level electrical charge upon contact. As Whiplash, he has made it his mission to destroy Tony Stark and everything he holds dear—including the Avengers!

EVIL PLAN

Revenge against Iron Man and his allies

VILLAIN STATS

HEIGHT:

6 FT. (1.83 M)

WEIGHT:

235 LB. (106.6 KG)

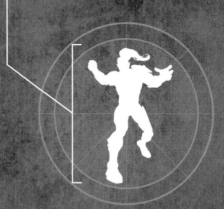

SPEED
Fast as a whip!

STRENGTH
Average, enhanced by armor

ABILITIES
Brilliant inventor and skilled combatant

WEAPON FILE: ENERGY WHIPS

To create his signature weapons, Vanko stripped out the wiring that powered the motors in Iron Man's armor and repurposed it into dual barbed whips spring-loaded into his gauntlets. In combat, Whiplash uses these electrically charged tendrils to deliver stunning blows as well as to confine his opponents.

MATERIAL:	ENERGY TYPE:	MAXIMUM LENGTH:
COPPER WIRE	**ELECTROMAGNETIC**	**25 FT. EACH** (7.62 M)

EARTH'S MIGHTIEST QUIZ!

Think you know the Avengers and their foes?
Time to put your top-secret knowledge to the test!

1. Nick Fury is the director of:
- A. Hydra
- B. The Avengers
- C. S.H.I.E.L.D.
- D. Award-winning movies

2. To stay alive, the Red Skull stole:
- A. Cap's shield
- B. Iron Man's armor
- C. Thor's hammer
- D. Ultron's robotic body

3. The Falcon's flight armor is code-named:
- A. Project Redwing
- B. The Hulkbuster
- C. The Iron Falcon
- D. J.A.R.V.I.S.

4. Technopathic powers let M.O.D.O.K.:
- A. Read minds
- B. See the future
- C. Change shapes
- D. Control machines

5. The real name of Thor's hammer is:
- A. Mjolnir
- B. MacDougal
- C. Mr. Meow
- D. Mick Jagger

6. Attuma is a warlord from:
- A. Atlanta
- B. Atlantis
- C. Attilan
- D. Allentown

7. Black Widow's weapons include:
- A. Multipurpose gauntlets
- B. Electrically charged batons
- C. Deadly combat skills
- D. All of the above

8. Captain America got his powers from:
- A. A nanovirus
- B. Super-Soldier Serum
- C. The Infinity Formula
- D. Gamma radiation

9. A.I.M. stands for:
- A. Attacking Iron Man
- B. Always Into Menacing
- C. Advanced Idea Mechanics
- D. Awesome Intelligence, M.O.D.O.K.!

10. The Hulk's human identity is:
- A. Steve Rogers
- B. Clint Barton
- C. Bruce Banner
- D. Emil Blonsky

11. Hydra's slogan is:
- A. "Hydra Assemble!"
- B. "Go, Hydra, Go!"
- C. "Hydra SMASH!"
- D. "Hail Hydra!"

12. Tony Stark did not design:
- A. The Hulkbuster
- B. J.A.R.V.I.S.
- C. Thor's hammer
- D. The Aven-Jet

13. Ultron wants to rid the world of:
- A. Humans
- B. Evil
- C. Robots
- D. Taxes

14. Hawkeye's weapons of choice are:
- A. Repulsor rays
- B. Trick arrows
- C. Exploding flechettes
- D. Energy whips

15. The Super-Adaptoid was created by:
- A. Justin Hammer
- B. Tony Stark
- C. A.I.M.
- D. Ultron

16. Falcon's wings are made from:
- A. Real falcon feathers
- B. Steel-mesh
- C. Vibranium
- D. Hard light

ANSWERS: 1C, 2B, 3A, 4D, 5A, 6B, 7D, 8B, 9C, 10C, 11D, 12C, 13A, 14B, 15A, 16D